# Stories Tales or Lies
# That Farmers Have Told Me

J.S. Maykut

# ACKNOWLEDGEMENTS

Dedicated to all the farmers past and present.  A sincere appreciation to those farm folk for their contributions of these stories and tales.

Thank you to Angele Black for her art sketches.

# Table of Contents

# INTRODUCTION

All names, places, preamble and front dressing to these stories and tales are fictional to protect the innocent. Your judgment as mine, as to the true happenings of these humorous tales, is yours to decide.

In my travels across the Western Canadian provinces over the years, I was reminiscing about these stories and tales that I heard from farming folks in their rural communities. Some of these tales may be gospel while others are stretched and brightly coloured or even lies. As time passes, many of these epic tales have grown by exaggeration or retold by a vivid imagination.

The early pioneers, from what I have gathered, had many a great story to tell, which in today's rural environment is sadly missing. In the old days there were many colourful characters, no special interest groups or human rights activists to curtail the human tendency to be a prankster.

I have felt some responsibility to document some of these stories, as they are part of our Western Canadian folklore, and also that others may enjoy a good chuckle.

J.S. Maykut

# You Need An Appointment

I'll just call him John. Hard working and honest, he never asked for anything more than a fair shake. He was a typical western farmer whose sense of humour was displayed by a mere reversal of a previous situation.

Spring arrived early. A meadowlark sang it's unbroken song as it sat upon a weathered corner fence post. It was these simple things that kept John and his wife Irene on the farm. Their four children had ventured to other fields of employment but always returned where their family roots were deeply planted. "I walked to the corner to pick up the mail," John stated in his mono-tone voice. "There was this important looking letter from the Department of Transportation. At lunchtime my dear wife read the letter to me a couple of times. The department wanted to expropriate some of our land to widen an adjacent highway. We decided that would be in the best interest for all. They requested that we come into the city to sign the documents. A week or so passed and leaving much necessary spring work behind, the wife and I ventured to the city and made a call on the department. They had a darn fancy office, with a pleasant young secretary who wanted to know our business. We showed her the letter and were surprised to hear that we would need an appointment. Enough seen and enough said, we headed home.

It was around two weeks later, I was out plowing up some sod when lo and behold, I see these two fellows dressed in suits with their ties flapping in the wind.

Sunday shoes they wore, as they high stepped over the freshly laid down furrows towards me. My dog Fritz led the way. They waved me down and told me that they were from the Transportation Department and had papers for me to sign. I just told them to make an appointment and kept on plowing."

# A Way With Dogs

The morning air was crisp. My bones told me that fall was soon approaching. I was driving a 1980 rust beaten Toyota and wanted to call on a farmer who was advertising an old tractor which was of interest to me, a 1950 John Deere model "M". It was a hot commodity, so many collectors in antique tractor clubs would also be making the call. I wanted to arrive early and take a peek. The ad also advised interested buyers to call in the evenings as he worked off the farm during the day. Wanting to be first on the scene, I followed the directions carefully. From a crest of a hill I could see an old farm yard that looked like the place. As I neared the yard I noticed the "M" behind a broken down shed. A large clump of willow hung over the rustic relic.

As I turned into the farm lane, I was greeted by a large German shepherd and could see that he meant business. The dog was on a long leash that was tethered from an overhead cable that ran at a diagonal across the yard. As my car came to a stop that hound charged and bounced off the driver door window. I had a front row seat and could see that the shepherd had all his teeth and that they were in fine working order! I decided that I had better leave.  Halfway down the lane I heard a loud thump.  Stopping, I soon realized that the dog's leash was attached to the back of my car.  The leash had wrapped itself around the car's drive shaft. There was the dog, winched tight up under the rear bumper.  The dog appeared deader then a stone!  Freeing the lifeless hound I placed him along the laneway.  I opened his mouth and yanked on his tongue.  I had the thought of giving him mouth to mouth but seeing his teeth, I decided that wasn't such a good idea.

To tell you the truth I was starting to panic.  I had killed the farmer's dog!  As a last resort, I pumped down on shepherd's chest three or four times.  To my surprise, the dog started to breath.  I reattached his leash and left.

That evening I returned to deal on the tractor.  The shepherd saw my rusty Toyota  coming down the lane and left in a hurry to the far end of the yard and laid down with his head down between his two front paws.  My knock on the back porch door soon brought a startled farmer with a greeting of  "How did you get past my dog, Jake?"  My quick reply was "I just have a way with dogs."  "I bought that junk yard beast for a good dollar to protect the place.  Nobody has ever gotten out of their vehicle and walked up these steps," replied the farmer.  Smiling, I shrugged my shoulders.  I did buy the old John Deere, but now it sits rusting, unfinished in my yard.

# The Threshing Crew

Activity across the plains was as brisk as a beehive prior to the on coming days of winter. It was harvest time. The eight-foot binder pulled by a pair of gentle giants Clydedales was a common site. Rows of stooked sheaves covered the countryside as they dried under the autumn sun. Many farmers waited for the threshing crew to complete the final task of separating the golden grain from their stalks.

Ben Simpson was a large robust, man and one of the original homesteaders of the district. He and his son were the proud owners of a new thirty six inch threshing machine called the 'Red River Special'. Persuaded by his neighbours, the new owners entered the custom threshing business. Ben hired many of his customers that were his neighbours to help in his new threshing venture. His pre-requisites were that they be hard working men with good horses. Ben being more then fair put his neighbour's needs first, therefore his farm was the last to be threshed in the season.

Rufus was a tall gangly man, with a scrawny hairy neck fitted with a protruding Adam's apple. The threshing crew called him

Roost as he resembled an immature cock rooster. Sparse tuffs of facial hair and a sly grin by were Rufus' calling card. He was known for his outlandish tomfoolery. Nevertheless, he was a diligent worker and had a fine team of horses. Rufus was hired on. Threshing was on it's first day on the Simpson farm. It was customary at day's end that a hearty meal was provided for the hard working harvest crew. Mrs. Simpson spared no expense as the meal of beef barley soup, roast beef, mashed potatoes and the assortment of steaming vegetables sat waiting on her kitchen table. Aroma from freshly baked pies filled the room.

"It was a good day fellows," commented Ben as his wife Beth filled the soup bowls. Small talk and chatter were the norm as each savored the tasty broth. Rufus was ready to execute his plan. Baby field mice were in abundance under the stooks, and Rufus had tucked several in his shirt pocket. Unnoticed, he put one in his mouth and started coughing. Slapping his hand down hard on the table he pulled a tiny pink baby mouse by it's tail from his mouth and tossed it across the table for all to see. "I see the Simpson's are hard up for grub!" he announced. Unnerved, Rufus continued to finish his soup as the rest of the crew excused themselves in a hurry from the table. A brave soul helped poor Mrs. Simpson as she had fainted and collapsed when she saw the baby mouse crawling across the table and into the butter dish!

# An Old Gent And Gophers

It was mid summer when I drove into a small Saskatchewan town and saw an elderly gentleman sitting on a bench with a walking cane lying across his lap. I needed directions and this appeared to be the only visible resident who may be of help. His name was William or as he told me later, folks just called him Bill. I was told that I was over twenty miles off course by taking a left turn instead of a right on the highway some miles back. Taking the wrong turn became a blessing in disguise.

"Do you have a few minutes to chew the rag?" Bill asked. "Why I guess I could," I responded. The few minutes turned into hours and the day ended as I watched a spectacular sunset over a vast open prairie.

I soon found out that Bill was a better salesman than I was. His early life as a young boy tweaked my interest. I was convinced in no time to drive him out of town some thirty five miles to view his childhood homestead where he had farmed. "See over there, the old barn is all that is left," chirped Bill. We drove down an old lane guarded by rows of the resilient caragana. "Back over there on that knoll stood our house," Bill said, pointing to the

15

spot now covered by tall waving grasses. As soon as the car stopped, Bill got out but tossed his cane back into the car. His arthritis seemed to remain there as well. His step got lighter as we walked. By returning to the homestead I could see Bill being rejuvenated with each step as we strolled over the old farmyard. The rest of the afternoon the old gentleman did the talking while I listened.

"I never wore shoes in the summer months out here, my parents couldn't afford them. I remember one summer my two cousins from town came out for a couple of weeks. It was back in the thirties and bone dry. The whole darn countryside was covered with dry grass, dust and gophers. My Dad said he'd take us to town for ice cream if we could catch a hundred gophers. The three of us had it figured out. We found some binder twine in the barn and made snares. As soon as one of them little varmints poked their heads out of their burrows we gave the twine a good yank. Head first they would go into an old worn out rubber boot and then dumped into our gunnysacks. At suppertime in came the gunnysacks with the live varmints! I remember my mother telling us boys to leave the gophers in the porch. We were eating at the kitchen table and telling my Dad of our successful catch when the whole kitchen exploded with scrambling terrified gophers! They were sliding and scurrying on the slippery linoleum floor. My Dad was up a - kicking and a- stomping with his big boots at the fast moving critters." Bill's laughter again filled the old homestead. "Out the front and back doors those gophers flew. My mother had the broom out and was swatting gophers as they scrambled around the whole house. I think us boys got more swats from my mother's broom hitting our rear ends then them gophers," Bill chuckled. It was right there and then that the old gent was a boy again as he flung his arms wildly and hopped around on the prairie sod, shooing out phantom gophers from the now gone kitchen.

On our way back to town the old gent fell fast asleep. His parting words are still with me. "I am part of this land and the land is my spirit." I couldn't have agreed more.

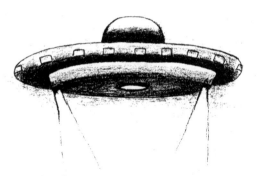

# Lights From a UFO

Truth or an illusion? From the countryside reports of flying saucers landing with little green men, filled the small town coffee shops. Some seers took oaths that what they had seen was gospel. He was a respected man in the community and his encounters with the mysterious lights were eerie and intriguing. His name was Tom, in his mid fifties. Silver grey hair adorned his temples accompanied by piercing steel blue eyes. Wearing a well worn baseball cap and with burly arms folded across his chest gave him a sense of credibility. Tom was a hard working no nonsense man. His neighbours could attest to that. He told me this story.

" It was the end of April and I was seeding spring wheat. It was getting dark and I still had over forty acres to go." Taking a deep breath and with a stern face Tom continued, "Looking towards the end of the field I noticed headlights. It was my neighbor Victor who had come to chat and see how I was doing, but more importantly to ask me to attend a range patrol meeting. Victor left after a hour or so and it was now quite dark." Rubbing his eye and clearing his throat, Tom continued. "I refueled and reloaded the drill with seed and fertilizer. I'm in my tractor cab having a farmer's supper of a sandwich and coffee, when I see these lights. That must be Victor I thought. What the heck did he forget, I said to myself. Then it happened," Tom whispered in a clear firm voice. "What happened?" I asked as I waited in anticipation. "Well, I don't know that I should tell you. When I told a few neighbours they thought I was on the sauce," Tom said quietly, but I prodded Tom to continue. "Before I could finish my coffee these lights were above the tractor cab and the radio went wild with static. I really didn't have a clue what was going on, just as quickly the radio was back to normal. Stumped and still wondering what those lights could be and thinking all was clear, I started to seed." "Is that it?" I asked. "No", came a firm reply from Tom as he removed his cap and gave his hair a run through with his fingers. "I wish it was. I was half way down the field when the radio went wild again. I could see the lights above the tractor again. What happened next still gives me the willies." Tom now had my full attention. I knew something extraordinary had taken place. "Did you hear any noise?" I asked. "Nothing above the tractor motor," was Tom's quick reply. "So what happened next?" I asked. Taking a deep breath the storyteller went on with his tale, "Out of the night sky a beam of red, yellow greenish light starts probing the side of the cab and tractor every six inches or so, and then comes a new colour that I have never seen before. The radio had gone berserk with static! In less then a couple of minutes everything was back to normal, except for me! My heart was a pumping but I wanted to finish seeding as rain was in the forecast. As I started seeding on another pass, the probe light was back again only this time checking out the other side of the rig. The radio again went ballistic. The hairs on the back of my neck bristled! The tractor started to sputter and then stalled as the blinking light continued its probe. What was out there? What did it want of me? I realized that it played havoc with the radio and now maybe the tractor's electrical system. I could see the probing light was zooming in for another pass. I decided there and then to get the hell out of there. I ran full tilt for my pick-up. My nearest neighbour was over five miles away. Holy Moses! In my hasty departure I left my jacket and keys in the tractor. The coast now seemed clear. I had no choice but to make a speedy dash and retrieve the keys. I don't think my legs ever moved so fast. Shaking, I fired up my pick up. I could see in the distance the probe lights returned at the far end of the field and were now following the fence line. I headed for the safety of my home all the while checking for overhead lights but never looking back." Tom now looked relaxed as he tapped his fingers to a tune on the kitchen table. "How about a coffee?" asked Tom, which I graciously accepted. "I still don't know if I believe in UFO's, said Tom, but what ever came down out of the sky that night still scares the beejeebers out of me. What I do know is that two inch of rain had given the untarped wheat and fertilizer a good soaking." "Is that it?" I asked. "That's it," replied Tom as he stirred a spoonful of sugar into his coffee.

# The Three R's

These are the days I fondly remember. The wind swept prairie plains of southern Saskatchewan is where I learned so well the three "R"s. It was a one-room schoolhouse situated on top of a gentle rise over looking a deep ravine filled with small willows and wolf willow shrubbery. Not far from the school an old wooden granary served as a stable for the horses of the children who came by buggy, cutter or bare back. I came on Belle, a black mare that had speed to spare. Not even the Model-T or newer model A's on the country roads were a match for Belle.

My parents were strict disciplinarians and knew the rules well. When I needed to be brought up by my bootstraps my father had his favorite. He'd shout, "for doing that my son, you better cover your eyes or I'll rip them out." Automatically and with great speed, I had both hands covering my eyes and what followed were wallops on my backside. The punishment administered came unseen with the delivery area unprotected. My mother was much gentler. She told me as a child that if I was lying she could always tell because my eyes would turn purple.

One day in that little old school house, in first grade, I told a big, big fib that my teacher, along with classmates believed. I went around most of that day in school asking everyone I could, "what color are my eyes?" To my surprise they all said, "your eyes are brown."

I recall on many cold days, as I rode Belle to school and not always having mittens, my hands would turn numb from the biting wind. To keep them warm I'd tuck them under Belle's mane. When riding into a stiff wind, I'd ride backwards to protect my face and my hands were at the nearest warmest spot, which was under her tail. Arriving at the schoolyard riding backwards was no great feat, but I noticed that those days my lunches had an off taste.

Classes were from grades one to nine with one teacher trying to do her best. At times, the older classmates would help us younger children learn how to read. One of the older boys by the name of Paul would always comment to the young girls that they looked awful pretty. Many of the older girls didn't seem to appreciate the compliment. I realized many years later that being awful and pretty was a contradiction at best.

There's one day I'll never forget as it brings me a big chuckle. Years previous, we had a young miss of a teacher who fit very well both in the community and with all students. I remember her name as Miss McDonald. It was not long before this beloved teacher was swept off her feet by a northern Saskatchewan farmer and soon married. Her replacement was a spinster in her mid forties, as tough as nails, high strung and who had the peculiar habit of chewing chalk when the classroom became too lively. I had advanced in grade and this was my second term with the Spinster, which was what we all called her when out of ear shot. The beginning of this school day I was in high spirits as my booty of crow and magpie legs, along with gopher tails would finance a new hockey stick from the government paid bounties. I saddled Belle and was off to school. The fall morning air was crisp under an azure sky, dappled with white clouds that lazily drifted towards the western horizon. An over night frost deposited diamond crystals on the tops of the tall grasses and a gentle breeze swayed them about like crowned dancing ballerinas. My mind drifted as I rode with my thoughts of playing shinny with my pals on the soon to be frozen ponds. My English grammar lesson from the Spinster this day was the proper usage of 'is and are.' "Remember this simple rule she said, 'Is' is to be used as singular or one, and 'are' is plural when referring to more then one." With the chalk still in the Spinster's hand I raised mine to ask the question. "Is it," I asked "is soles or are soles?" The Spinster was not amused. As my classmate's giggled, I was quickly taken by the ear to the front of the classroom where I received my punishment by holding out my hand. News travelled home faster than a prairie grass fire. I was greeted by my mother who told me in a soft voice that my father wanted to talk to me about some schoolwork or lesson of some sort. I received my punishment with a smile. I heard my parents discuss this event in their bed that night to the accompaniment of laughter.

# The Summer Community Picnics

Most every district in the rural communities held a summer picnic. They were generally held on a weekend of the summer months of July and August. All residents of the area from the small fry to the elderly were participants. Three-legged-sack and wheel-barrel races had many a spill, but most importantly they all ended with laughter. Competition was fierce among local ball teams as they pitted their skills and coaching maneuvers that crowned the winners with bragging rights. These community events owed their great success to volunteers and of course the enticing country fare.

Isaac Finlay, a bachelor, sat on the back porch steps of his small farm house with a grin as wide as a flat-ended spade as he reminisced about past picnics. With a devilish twinkle in his eye and his face covered with silver stubble he proceeded to tell the following story.

"Remember old Fritz Hankerman?" he began, as he loaded his bottom lip with some fresh snuff. "He was a little short fellow with his ass no more than a foot or two off the ground and built like a barrel. He always strutted the grounds like a proud peacock with no place to go. Fritz ....he never failed to boast about his donated homemade wiener snitzels and claimed that there were none better. A couple of local lads and I were in charge that year of Fritz's wieners. I was no more then eleven or twelve years old. We had a hundred or so wieners in a large black cast iron pot that was fired by a blowtorch. The fuel in that torch must have contained some water. Mimicking a small dragon, it coughed, spit and hissed. We were on a roll! The pot came to a boil, and within a minute or two all the folks on the picnic grounds, including the farm dogs, could smell the fumes coming off those wieners. I must say they smelled good. Real good. Fritz's wieners sold then for a nickel with a buttered homemade bun and mustard included. Every year his wieners sold out and that made Fritz darn happy.

This one-year we rigged up a plan for old Fritz Hankerman. I took a large leather-stitching needle from home along with some butcher string and had it woven in and out of a wiener especially doctored for Fritz. I did have the help of my two friends Paul and Benjamin. A line of customers soon formed and Fritz was fourth or fifth in line chatting and of course doing a great deal of bragging. Paying his nickel, Fritz soon had his special wiener wrapped in the bun and loaded with mustard. Before he took the first bite, I remember he had a look in his eye like a goat ready to chew on a fresh green thistle. "Made in heaven," he bellowed in his thunderous voice, so all could hear. What followed still gives me a big belly laugh. He put over half of that string stitched wiener snitzel in his mouth and bit down hard followed with a yank. To everyone's surprise, including us young lads, out came Fritz's false teeth locked well into the wiener. Teeth and all went sailing through the air for ten or twelve feet before landing on the ground in a small puff of dust. No sooner had they hit the ground, a local farm dog ran off with the whole mess. "Come here you son-of-a-bitch," he hollered as the dog ran away with it's prize. "You damn varmint! I'll skin you alive," he shouted as he chased the hound over the picnic grounds amid the laughter of picnic goers. With some gentle coaxing, Fritz finally convinced the dog to give him back his munchers, minus of course the wiener. This wasn't the end for us young lads, as he threatened to have us castrated before the day was out! In less than an hour however, Fritz was back with his teeth rinsed, reset and smiling as if nothing had happened. "I'm hungry," he whispered in a mild voice. With straight but guilty faces we gave him two of his homemade wieners at no charge. "You young lads pulled a good one on me," he said as he came around and patted us on our backs. Assuming forgiveness, we were quite taken back when Fritz delivered a few swift kicks to our backsides. I must say they landed fair and square! Fritz's punishment just made us hoot and holler and laugh much louder. Of course we were spared the promised castration.

As the years passed, the distance Hankerman's false teeth flew continued to increase. Bill Clarkson, who farmed down the road a couple miles, told folks that when those teeth spun through the air, they whistled for the dog and landed some forty feet away. Some folks also said that the dog wore Fritz's teeth for over an hour trying it's best to chew down that wiener. Fritz Hankerman, I must say, was a good sport and a benefit to the community."

# The Tale of an Early Weed Inspector

I served in the RCAF during WWII and with my release the government offered me free university tuition or a homestead farm. I chose the university but I eventually ended up farming. After completing my second term of schooling I landed a summer job as a Weed Inspector. To my surprise, after I accepted the job, I found out I needed a vehicle. With the goodness of my father's financing, I purchased a ten year old 1936 International half ton that today we'd call a pick-up. The truck was as sound as a rock and never abandoned me as I made the rounds visiting farmers. I now think many farmers felt a bit sorry for me as I was a bit of a green horn. I was often invited into their homes for cookies and coffee that was generally followed with an abundance of BS supplied by me. The weed control chemical that was very new to most farmers was 2-4D Ester. I was supplied with a two-gallon hand sprayer and went about the county demonstrating how effective 2-4D was at killing weeds. This truly was a government job!

I awoke one morning to the sweet smell of fresh cut hay. A light breeze gently played with the curtains as they seemed to beckon me to the start of a new day. Outside I found the western sky stacked with rolling black clouds edged with tuffs of white cotton. It looked like rain. I had rented a small country cottage. The property had a two seater out back that I now ran towards to beat the approaching storm. No sooner had I settled down with catalog in hand that I was greeted with a loud clap of thunder and rain. What happened still amazes and frightens me today. As I was turning a page, a bolt of lightning followed by a deafening bang, blew me off my perch! The door flew open and hung on one hinge. The smell of burnt wood filled the air. With my breeches still around my ankles, I headed as fast as I could for safer ground. I can honestly say it scared the crap right out of me.

# A Farm Call With the Local Vet

The summer monsoons had arrived and little fieldwork could be done under these wet conditions. I had no trouble convincing myself that the weeds and farm calls could wait since I was working for the government. I drove into the nearest town and while sitting in the tavern, I soon became acquainted with the local veterinarian, Wolfe. He was a big man and I would have fit nicely under his armpit. Having quenched our thirst, Wolfe with his husky drawl invited me along on one of his farm calls, which I accepted. "We're going to Schmidt's farm. He dropped by my office this morning and said one of his fresh milk cows was down. Just milk fever I presume. If you want to see manure, this is the place," quipped Wolfe. No sooner had we turned into the farmyard, there was farmer Schmidt dressed in patched bib overalls and gumboots waving us over to the barn. "She's lying down in the last stall. Can't get her up. She's been down since yesterday morning. I'd hate to loose her. Hell, she's one of my better cows." Schmidt's face was filled with concern as he continued to chatter as we walked into the barn. "Looks like milk fever, that's what we have here," said Wolfe quietly. After doing his examination and doctoring the downed animal, he went on to explain to Schmidt that the sick cow would be up and around in a couple of hours. "What's the damage?" Schmidt asked in a relieved voice. "That will be a total of ten dollars, five for my call and five for the dope," said the vet. Schmidt reached into his pocket and handed Wolfe a five-dollar bill and also a five-dollar bill to me. Surprised, I tucked the bill in my pocket and said, "thanks!"

On our way back to town I offered the money to Wolfe, which he would not accept. That big vet just laughed all the way back to town. He insisted farmer Schmidt's thinking that I was the attending dope, was worth more than the fin. I still have that five-dollar bill framed in my den.

# A Tale From A Watkins Salesman

William McKinley was born and raised in the district. To supplement his farm income he travelled the area far and wide selling Watkins products. Bill, as he was known by most of his customers, was a very jovial man. Care and compassion were his attributes as he helped many poorer folks by offering them free products or extended credit. He sported a large handle bar moustache and greeted everyone with a warm smile. Sitting in his rocking chair and puffing on a short stub of a cigar, his face lit up as he began retelling a few tales from his years of travel.

"Hell, I sold or gave away enough salves and ointments to run this country without an ache or squeak that would last for more then ten years. I had cure-all ointments for sore joints to be used on a man or on his horse. Salves that would heal cuts and wounds in a matter of a few days. A special salve for healing the blisters on the teats of a milk cow was one of my biggest sellers. The salves I sold did the trick. Most folks called me the snake oil salesman yet they always reordered when they ran out or were running low." Clearing his throat and taking a deep breath, he paused a moment and relit his cigar. "I had this one ointment

35

that I always recommended. I told everyone who bought it that they should rub it in good on whatever was hurting. Well, to my surprise, I found this not to be quite the truth. You see, this one farmer, whose name I believe was Mack Simonsen, found this ointment a little on the hot side. He told me that he labored hard one day picking and moving large rocks from his summer fallow field. Mack was a hard worker and stronger than a bull. Nothing or nobody stood in his way, and if they did, they usually got run over with no questions asked. No nonsense was the name of his game." Removing the cigar and wiping his mouth with his sleeve, Bill rose slowly from his chair and yawned as if this was the end of the story. Taking a stretch like an awakening cat and scratching his protruding belly, he soon sat down in his rocker and continued telling the tale.

"Well I'm lucky to be alive, as Mack said he would have killed me if I had been there. These were Mack's exact words. I was pushing hard on this big rock. I wanted to roll it onto the stone boat. I guess, I pushed too hard and blew out my gasket! He had a case of what we'd call hemorrhoids on the back end. He told me he soaked that evening in the tub for an hour or more but had no relief. Then he thought of the ointment I sold him. As I had instructed, he applied it generously and rubbed it in. In a matter of minutes he was sitting on an inflamed ring of fire! I met Mack some two months later, and I was greeted by ... you-son-of-a-bitch! He appeared to be walking a bit bow legged. He never did order any more ointment."

# Haying With The Hired Man

I grew up on the open prairie along with my five siblings. My parents ran a small dairy farm and supplied the nearby village with milk. The farm and the surrounding countryside was nature's ideal playground. Creativity and open spaces were the only ingredients needed to fill our summer days before we went back to school. Tom and Luke, my two older brothers, were a pair of mischievous pranksters whose shenanigans provided many colorful memories.  This is just one of their pranks that comes to mind.

Otto was the hired man who helped with the hand milking and other farm chores. His nemeses were mainly my brothers Tom and Luke, and at times, the rest of us children. This day was very hot and cloudless.  There was not a breeze.  A redtail hawk circled above only to disappear as it flew into the path of the sun.  We were playing 'Aunty I Over' on an old granary behind the barn and our voices were accompanied by the shrill screams of the hawk as it watched us toss an old rubber ball over the rooftop. The game soon took its toll.  Hot and sweaty, we all headed for the livestock water trough where we jumped in and splashed about. It was a splendid way to cool off on such a hot day. Our laughter and shouts soon brought Otto out of the barn leading Billy and Bob, a team of giant grey Percherons. "You little brats get the hell out of there before I drown the whole bunch of you," Otto hollered. We knew he meant business and we fled for our lives and stood dripping wet on the porch steps.

Otto soon had the team of greys hitched to a hayrack and headed out to the field of cut hay. Enjoying the rumble noise of the steel wheels, we tagged along and hung onto the back of the hayrack dragging our bare feet through the dust on the road. The hay had been dump raked, giving the appearance of many loaves of brown bread scattered about on a large floor. Pitchfork in hand, Otto began the task of loading the hayrack. Bill and Bob moved from hay pile to hay pile under Otto's commands. We petted the horses' soft pink noses and offered them tufts of green grass. Tranquility and peacefulness reigned.

Under many hay piles were the homes of field mice. Tom and Luke accompanied by Tipper the farm dog, waged war on the scurrying small rodents. A couple of large mice were caught by my brothers who immediately deposited them under the horses tails. Otto soon sensed that something was wrong. The horses began acting up. "You get the hell away from there! Leave those horses alone. If I see any of you around them again, you'll be getting the end of my pitchfork," he hollered. We all scampered off to a safe distance and continued to watch from a small knoll. The mice were held in tight by a clamped down tail and only moved around once the pressure was released. The live deposits created sporadic havoc. Otto did numerous visual inspections but could not find out why the once so quiet team had become so uneasy and fidgety. Our prank soon came to an end as our four year old sister broke ranks and spilled the beans. I never ran so fast for the safety of home. That afternoon we all received our punishment as we were held head first in the rain barrel to our last breath, followed by a gasping…"I promise, never to… !" Spared from the dunking was the bean spiller who, to this day is still not forgiven.

# Saga Of A Moose Hunt

The air was crisp and clear and one's breath hung like a puff of smoke from a well worked cigar. Hoar frost appeared on the blades of the tall grasses, only to vanish quickly under the sun's mid-morning rays. It was that time of year again - moose hunting season.

My hunting partners and I gathered our gear and headed out the next day for the Slave River Flats, only known to us as 'The Moose Pasture Heaven.' On our arrival, we were greeted by a pair of Whiskey Jacks, other wise known as camp robbers. An outfitter's tent would be our home for the next week or two.

The campsite had a blanket of golden leaves, courtesy of a buff of poplar. At the side of a small clearing, four massive spruce trees extended their branches like welcoming arms as a gentle breeze swayed them back and forth. A red squirrel broke the silence as it chattered and scolded us for arriving. An outcropping of rocks were held in place by sturdy jackpines that covered a ridge to the north. At the base of the ridge, a small spring trickled down into a small pool only to disappear into the deeper depths of the earth. The scent of pine filled our nostrils as we set up camp at the base of the giant spruce. This to us was more than a hunt. It was our annual affair of down to earth male bonding.

Let me tell you a bit about my hunting partners. They were unique fellows. In camp each man had the opportunity to brag and boast of his pass hunts. Exaggerated tales were soon chopped up like fire wood and then dressed down with the abundance of laughter.

Gus Werner was the camp cook and overseer. He had never shot a moose, or any wild animal. He had a fear of getting lost and only hunted within 100 yards of the camp. Gus claims he has never missed a shot. That was true, especially when we are relaxing around the campfire, savoring the blends of fine scotch whiskey. Abraham McAllister on the other hand, was completely different. Abe was a keen adventurer. A few years back, Abe accidentally shot himself twice in the same day, all within an hour. He was learning about the "off and on" safety position on his new Winchester rifle. The first shot just grazed the sleeve of his parka. The second shot entered the front of his boot... luckily just going between his toes. Damage was minor but he did need a bit of patching up from old Doc Hendricks. To join our hunting party, he obtained permission from his wife Elsie under the strict conditions that all the ammunition be carried in his vest pocket. Gus and I faithfully held him to the promise.

Returning from the day's hunt we satisfied our hunger with Gus's hardy stew while sitting around the campfire reminiscing about our past glory days. As the night wore on more wood was added to the fire pit, which sent sparks from the top of the flames into the night sky joining the hanging stars above. This was the time and place for man to replenish his inner soul and self worth. The chorus voices of wolves broke the night silence and we all knew that their hunt was just begining. We retired to our sleeping bags and cots, as tomorrow was another day. Gus sipped on his favorite brand of scotch while he lingered by the campfire until its flickering death.

Before crawling into our sleeping bags, Abe and I turned Gus's cot end for end and turned out the gas lantern. We were soon engulfed by the blackness of night.

Our beloved camp cook soon awakened us as he struggled to get into his sleeping bag. "Did you-no-good-rotten-son-of-bitches sow the end of my bag shut? Who do you think is going to make you bastards breakfast in the morning? Hell, this is going too far." Gus continued to cuss and grumble calling us every name that came to mind. Now fully awakened and sitting up in our cots we suggested that Gus should go to the other end of his cot. "Gus if you stayed off that cheap Scotch you'd be able to find your way home," quipped Abe softly. Not another word was spoken as the night again regained its silence. Abe and I were greeted in the morning by the familiar smell of bacon and eggs and the aroma of brewing coffee.

A blanket of snow now decorated the landscape. All the forest's inhabitants large or small left their visible mark on the white sheet of snow laid down by Mother Nature.

To an experienced hunter the activity of the wildlife was now easily studied. Imprints on the fresh snow told the story of who they were, what they were doing and when they were there. To stay for a few more days we needed to replenish our larder with a few staples of coffee, beans and bread. As the crow flies, some ten or twelve miles due west, was a small village with a grocer. A democratic decision was made that I'd hike to the village early in the morning and pick up the necessary supplies. The alarm clock was set for 6:00 A.M. as it would be a three-hour walk.

Up at the sound of the ringing alarm, I dressed quickly and slipped on my backpack and headed out to fulfill my duty. A theatrical show in the sky welcomed me.

The northern lights danced and swirled above my head encouraging me to quicken my pace. To my surprise the village was in complete darkness and I was greeted only by barking dogs. Not a light shone in the store or a village home. To keep warm, I spent the next two to three hours pacing up and down the main street and the back lanes, doing my best to become acquainted with the resident hounds. Where was every one? Finally the store opened and I realized that my camp buddies had adjusted the clock three hours in advance. Upon my return to camp, I did not give Abe or Gus the satisfaction in knowing the results of their prank. We still continue our annual hunt, once the fall harvest is completed. Although I have taken many photos of moose from this valley, as yet none have found their way to my table.

# The Collector

I once ran a small agriculture business retailing farm supplies to the local farming community. Sales were slow. Farmers were struggling to make ends meet as farm commodity prices were low and drought had also inflicted additional hardship on the district. My accounts receivable were in good standing due to the circumstances. There were a small number of past due bills aged over a year or more, which were written off and deemed as bad debt.

This day the weather had turned nasty and a small blizzard howled outside. I was surprised to see an old beat up half-ton Ford turn into the driveway and stop directly in front of the office door. A balding, paunchy man dressed in an unbuttoned trench coat soon blew into my office along with the outside storm. He introduced himself as Walt Pedersen. He was looking for any type of job and claimed he had run into hard times. At first, I told him that I had nothing available as business was very slow. We chatted over a cup of coffee and some how I offered him a job for the collection of my written-off bad debts on a commission basis. With briefcase and paperwork in hand, Walt left just as he had come in, with whirling snow engulfing him as he headed for his truck.

It was not long after Walt dropped by the office and greeted me with firm handshake and broad smile. Curious, I asked. "How did it go?" "Better then I expected. This type of work is new and foreign to me," he said softly. Opening the briefcase, I could see that most statements had funds neatly attached. "You have done very well," I stammered in disbelief. "It was a struggle with some, but most farm folks paid up with the exception of a few. The account of Otis Kirkhauf was a bit of a tough one. I told him the same as others, that they must put something down or pay in full. The old geezer told me he was flat broke, flatter then a pancake. I continued to insist for over an hour that he must put something down or I wasn't going to leave. Well, he did put something down. He took out his false teeth and slapped them down on the kitchen table and told me that was all he owned. I kept my word. As soon as those dentures landed, I flipped them into my open briefcase and left." Smiling sheepishly, Walt reached into his coat pocket and handed me old Otis's munchers. Commission paid, I never did see Walt again.

The next day just before closing, I had a visit from Otis. He paid his bill in full and wanted his teeth back. A new pair would cost more than what was owed. Unfortunately, Walt did not collect his commission on the Kirkhauf account.

# A Visit To The Preacher

Bart Martin, an elderly man now in his early eighties, lived his life as a bachelor. He grew up and farmed in the district some five miles north of town. A few years ago, he sold the farm and became a resident of the local senior citizens home. Those who knew him just called him Bart. Faithfully each morning, stooped with cane in hand, he trudged down the street to a small café for a cup of coffee. This was the highlight of his day. It was the time to visit and chat with his farm buddies. George Freemont was his farming neighbour and knew Bart very well. In his farming years Bart had developed a few habits, some were good and some needed a bit of correction.

"I really liked Saturdays in my younger days. Hell, a man then could just do what he wanted." Looking at me with his infectious smile, Bart took a sip of coffee, always followed by wiping his lips with his sleeve. "You see, each Saturday after I had my chores done, I'd drive into town to the local tavern for my sampling of beer. As the time passed, I found out I was arriving earlier and leaving later." Bart's eyes twinkled as he scratched the bottom of his chin. "Soon I was there when they opened and was thrown out when they closed. To make matters a bit worse, my fine driving caught the eye of the local enforcement and my driver's licence in due time was lifted. Dang it, I must of had twenty or so tickets." Pausing a moment, Bart regained his thoughts and sighed. "I guess the only benefit was that I cleared the ditches from brush on my way home." Taking a glance out into the street and running his gnarled fingers through his hair, Bart took a deep breath and continued. "I had an old Fordson tractor and I started to drive that into town. I knew no one would need a licence to drive a tractor. Coming into town with my old Fordson tractor was a hell of an idea. Sorry to say it was short lived. The local establishment and Judge Brown were on to me. I was banned from driving any motorized vehicle down the roads. I still have the document somewhere," Bart chuckled as he waved the waitress over for a coffee refill. "Those boy's didn't have me yet," he exclaimed with a twinkle in his eye. "I went out and bought myself a pony and sturdy saddle. It was reliable, safe and cheap transportation. It didn't take long before that pony knew the way into town and back all on her own. Better then a taxi or any woman, that pony was." Bart eyes drifted to the floor to regain his line of thought, then he cracked his knuckles and continued. "I remember this one summer day very well. Of course it was a Saturday. I was running low on feed for my livestock so my morning was spent grinding grain. In my own mind, the dust from the grain made me a bit thirsty. My pony and I headed for town. As usual, I found my way into the beer parlor and I stayed there until dark. My transportation was tied up back. Having my fill, I found my way into the saddle and headed for home. On the outskirts of town there was a large tent in the sports grounds that caught my eye. There were fifty or so vehicles in the parking lot and folks milling around. What the heck is going on? I tied my pony to the nearest tree and was soon ushered into the tent. A pretty young lady took me by the arm and sat me down in the front row, right next to a small raised platform. She wore a big smile but she had a look in her eye similar to that of a monkey grinder. I was starting to feel at home. It wasn't too long that a preacher, dressed all in black, comes out and starts giving us folks the works of fire and brimstone. He strutted around like a small bantam rooster, raised his voice as if to crow, but started hollering, Hallelujah ... Hallelujah! This is the time to repent of your sins. Be made clean! Come forth and be saved! Satan wants your soul! From the folks came the words... Amen brother! Amen ! Amen! He also professed to be a healer and invited all with any aliments or sickness to come forth. Still under the influence, I was up on the stage in no time flat with the help of the pretty young lady that had seen me in. I told this preacher that my head hurt and instantly I found his hands placed on top my head asking the Almighty above to take away my pain. To my surprise, I was soon feeling much better. He then asked if there were any other problems. Being in the presence of a fiery preacher, I was not about to tell a lie. I looked him in the eye and announced quite loudly, making sure all could hear that I also had a bad case of diarrhea. He definitely did not place his hands where that problem was!" With closed eyes, Bart roared with laughter, and his shoulders rose and fell and kept rhythm with each chuckle. "I was quickly ushered from the tent, he continued. In the saddle on the way home, the preacher's words continued to ring in my head. Hallelujah, hallelujah. Come forth and be saved." The saddle on that pony was just like a rocking chair and before we had gone a half-mile, I fell asleep.

I awoke sitting in the saddle. My trusty pony had stopped in front of the barn.

It was time for his bucket of crushed grain. I opened the door to the feed bin. From the interior blackness of the grain bin two red eyes like burning lumps of coal, came right at me. In each hand I had hold of a horn. The devil had surely come to claim me! I slammed the door so hard that every board on the bin rattled. The devil snorted and stomped around inside making a hell of a ruckus. I wanted nothing to do with the devil in the middle of the night. The preacher was right. The devil had arrived at my place and had come to claim my soul!" Bart paused for a moment and grinned. "I never knew I could get up on a horse so fast. I was headed for my good neighbour George Freemont. I told George the whole tale, the tent, the preacher and to where I had the devil trapped in the feed bin. He knew I wasn't lying as my pony and I were covered in sweat! George fired up his truck and we drove down to my farmyard that night. Scared, I stayed in the half-ton as George made his way to the feed bin. He was a brave man, as he carried only a flashlight. I told George to be careful, as the devil was not one to be messed with. To my relief, it was a different type of devil that I had trapped. One of my yearling steers was the beast. Apparently I had neglected to close the bin door after grinding grain. The next morning I promised to the heavens above that the local beer parlor I would visit no more." Gently biting his bottom lip and beaming with a smile he knew his tale was told. "To this day I have been loyal to that promise," Bart said with closed eyes. I picked up the tab for our coffee. He clutched his cane and told me with a grin that he was off to see his girl friend!

# The Ranchers

Bud McVee and Tom Olsen were the proud owners of neighbouring ranches. Their voices drifted quietly over the pasture. Not far away a meadowlark, sitting on a gatepost, sang it's melody. The spring melt lay about in the low draws as green grasses started to appear around the edges. The prairie dog town was alive as alarmed barks rang out when a red tail hawk circled above. It was spring.

Bud leaned on a post, with the top nestled under his armpit. Tom, a few feet away on the other side of the fence, held the top strand of barbed wire and with one foot placed on the bottom strand, chatted over ranch happenings. "Yesterday was just about the day of reckoning for me. I had an old Simmental cross Angus cow that had a difficult time in dropping her calf. I ran her into the corral that had a snubbing post planted dead centre." Pausing, Bud took a roll-your-own from a small tin and lifting his leg to tighten his trousers, he struck a wooden match. "Well, I nailed her on my first throw and laid a half-hitch on the snubbing post. That old Bossy did a 360 and in a flash had her first wrap on me." Taking a long drag on his cigarette and blowing the smoke out of his nostrils, he continued. "Before long, she had four to five wraps on me. I was tied tight from my boots to a foot over my buckle. That ornery devil always circled to the right and the rope between her and me was getting shorter. The next thing I knew, she was blowing steam up my pant leg. Thank God, the only thing between her and me now was the post." Tom, in disbelief shook his head and murmured, "if I'd been drinking, I'd be on the cow's side." "Damn you; I stayed wrapped to that post for over three hours all the while hollering for the Mrs." "Looks like she came or the rope rotted," Tom quipped. "You'll get yours one of these days," replied Bud, solemn faced. "Well, the Mrs. did come finally, just because I was two hours late for supper. I must say that she was the most beautiful woman over fifty that I ever saw, when she came into that corral. The best part was that old bossy, dropped two healthy twin calves all the while I was hog tied." Now smiling and showing his rope burns from leg to waist, Bud stomped his cigarette stub into the moist ground. Bidding farewell with a firm handshake the ranchers agreed to meet the next day in Bud's corrals to doctor and brand a few calves.

The sound of bawling cows and calves echoed down the valley. Soon the air was filled with the smell of singed hair as brands were placed down on the newly born innocents. Young male offspring had their manhood, so to speak, removed. These prairie oysters were highly prized. Varying in size they were tossed into a bucket for the traditional gourmet feed.

"Tom, why are you branding these calves? Everyone knows they are yours. You're the only one raising scrubs," yelled Bud over the noise of continuous bawling as he handed over another hot branding iron. "Hell it wouldn't be worth one's time to steal mangy critters like these." Distracted by Bud's chatter, a calf freed a leg and delivered a direct hit sending Tom on his backside.

Tom's tin of Copenhagen snuff sailed through the air and was soon scooped up by one of the ranch hands. A ripped shirt with front pocket missing was now decorated with fresh calf manure. Disgusted and swearing a blue streak, Tom proceeded at the task of branding.

As dusk approached and the day's work done, it was now time to extinguish their thirst and sit around the campfire. The day's commotion and bawling was now replaced with boisterous chatter. Camaraderie among the ranchers and ranch hands had now begun. "Look what's coming," someone hollered. A baked pan of breaded prairie oysters arrived as appetizers to a hungry crew. "Hey Tom, since you're the rightful owner of these dandy ranch grown oysters, this large one is especially reserved for you. You did a hell of a job of branding," Bud chuckled as he handed Tom a skewed oyster. With a beer in hand and a "gee thanks" the fun began. "This nut is darn tough," Tom mumbled as he rolled the morsel around in his mouth. He soon realized that he had been had. "You bastards gave me a raw one. Where is my tin of snuff? It's one way to kill that taste." Tom caught his favorite tin as it came flying his way out of the darkness. Under the glow of the campfire with a fresh beer and a large wad of snuff placed under his bottom lip, Tom sat down with a sigh of relief and stared into the flames of the fire. "This snuff kind of tastes funny, more like horse shit," Tom moaned. He realized that he had been had again. "What friends and neighbours would feed you a raw prairie oyster and mix horse shit in your snuff?" he wondered. A good mouth rinse of beer followed by a ranch raised barbequed steak was all that was needed to bring back Tom's smile. He knew that he was surrounded by his true friends that cared and knowing there would always be a time for sweet retribution.

# The Old Brown Suitcase

The sounds of angry crows in the early morning hours woke Pete Straka from his deep sleep. His wife Stella remained motionless beside him, unaware of the outdoor ruckus. Peering out the bedroom window, he saw a large owl perched in a tree that over hung the garage. Twenty to thirty pesky crows continued to torment their nighttime enemy. "Too bad it wasn't my banker sitting up there," Pete thought to himself. It was too early to rise and the thought of the day's farm work soon left his mind and he again returned into the land of slumber.

"What's on your agenda today?" Stella asked as she poured her husband a fresh cup of coffee that was accompanied with a plate of scrambled eggs and hash browns. "Oh, I really don't know for sure. I left the tractor and plough last night on the quarter down the road. I figured to finish ploughing this morning in a couple of hours. Why do you ask?" Pete waited for an answer as his wife returned to the stove with the empty frying pan. "Maybe if you're not too busy, we could run into town this afternoon. I need to buy a few groceries and do a bit of shopping." Sitting down at the kitchen table across from her husband, Stella smiled warmly as Pete began wolfing down his breakfast. "That's fine with me," he said. "If you could run me down the road, I'll finish the ploughing and then treat you to a lunch in town." Pete grinned as he worked a toothpick along the top row of his teeth. "You have yourself a deal my man, you have yourself a deal." Stella smiled as she followed Pete out the door, clutching the keys to their half-ton truck. "I had a dream last night that the banker was driving our tractor to an auction sale. I can see that it's still here hooked to the three bottom. Guess I can still dream as it hasn't cost me a cent," Pete chuckled as he stepped from the half-ton and up on to the tractor. Waving each other good byes, the job to finishing the ploughing began.

"What the heck is going on," Pete whispered to himself with his chin held close to his chest. The tractor began to cough and sputter and soon died. "I'll be dammed," Pete moaned. Upon inspection, the problem was simple. No gas. The tank was dry. "I know the tank was near full when I shut down last night," Pete mumbled to himself in disgust, lifting his cap and gently giving his scalp a light scratch. He knew that some culprit or culprits had siphoned the gas. Under the mid morning sun, Pete slowly plodded the one mile home. That day the promised lunch to Stella was kept. In time the ploughing was done. The Straka's were not the only farm family to experience missing gasoline from their farm vehicles. As time passed it seemed that if things were not nailed down, they went missing. Word soon spread among the local farmers. Names of suspects, guilty or not, were tossed about. Pete Straka and his neighbor Frank Wilson devised a plan.

"I think it's some of those punk lads from town that are driving them souped up jalopies. Who else would pinch a few tools and gas?" queried Frank. I heard some folks call them kids with slicked grease hair and bellowed pants, Zoot Suiters. There's a pair in town that look too slick for me." "Could very well be them," Pete nodded. "I've a big old mama skunk hanging around my chicken coop. This morning, I picked up a live trap box from the county office and I'll have that stinking varmint before dusk. We'll run old smelly into a suit case and deposit the package along the roadside a couple of miles out of town." Beaming from ear to ear, Frank received the approval of his plan by Pete's nodding. "Folks tell me, just about every evening just before dark that a hot jalopy roars out of town. There's an empty farm yard, that old Millers place. We'll leave the suitcase at the entrance, right next to that old mail box." "Mighty fine plan, Frank. Who's putting the mama skunk in the suitcase? Don't count on me. Stella claims I smell bad enough," said Pete grinning. "Leave that up to me. I'll pick you up tomorrow," replied Frank.

As Frank had promised the suitcase was loaded and deposited at the entrance to the Miller's lane. They proceeded down the road and waited out of sight. The wait was not long. The hot jalopy screeched to a halt and the bait was taken. Their prize was not kept for long. The jalopy came to a sudden stop as two young lads bailed out for fresher air. "Looks as if the perfume in the hot rod is not to the boy's liking," smirked Frank. "I see the scoundrels are hoofing it back to town. That was a hell of a plan, Frank, a hell of plan." Smiling, Pete took a swig from a bottle of whiskey that they had been nursing and patted his neighbor firmly on the back. For some strange reason, the disappearances stopped, and life returned to normal in the farming community.

# Love In The Air

Two large crabapple trees dressed in their finest spring attire of whites and pinks filled the air with a sweet fragrance. Bees hummed and buzzed the airways as they transported nectar and pollen to a nearby hive under the shade of a weeping willow. Red-breasted robins busily collected dry grasses and mud for their new home being built on an open wooden beam in the woodshed. Brutus, the farm hound lay stretched out at the base of the front steps fast asleep and oblivious to his surroundings. This was the homestead and farm of John and Mary Rimstead. Zach and Abe were their sons. The Rimsteads were law-abiding citizens and regular Sunday churchgoers.

In the district, around five miles away as the crow files, farmed the family of Philip and and Sadie McNab. The McNabs sported five lovely daughters; Sally, Susan, Sara, Shirlee and Sonja. They ranged in age from ten to eighteen. Philip held a tight reign on his daughters as many a young man eyed these blue-eyed blonde beauties. The two families met each Sunday at regular church services. What one family had, the other desperately wanted. The Rimsteads yearned to have a daughter while the McNabs wished for a son.

Playing at the local town theater was "Gone With The Wind" staring Clark Gable and Vivian Leigh. In the countryside the show was the talk of the community especially amongst the younger folk. It was not long before the Rimstead boys arranged dates with the two eldest McNab girls following a Sunday church service. Abe and Zach drove the family sedan to the Rimsteads with Brylcreem laden hair and smiles of anticipation. "I know that Sue is really sweet on me. As soon as I asked her, she said yes and then ran off and giggled. I think Sue is the prettiest of the bunch. What do you think my big brother?" asked Zach. "She is pretty, but I'll stick to Sally. She is the smartest and I'll take my chances with her with no questions asked," replied Abe as he guided the car out of the lane onto the road. "Well I'm taking Sue up into the balcony and before the end of the show, we'll be a kissing I'm sure," smirked Zach. "When she slaps your face, how are you going to explain the red welts and bloody nose? You're no Romeo. The best I seeing you doing is holding her hand," laughed Abe as he gave his younger brother a light swat at the back of his head. As the drive continued Abe's and Zach's romantic exploits grew with each mile. They acted like two young pre-schoolers eager to find the prize at the bottom of a Cracker Jack box as soon as it was open. Within the car, euphoric romance reigned.

On the veranda sat Philip Rimstead, shirtless. His bare chest being covered only by soiled red suspenders. At his feet lay his faithful friend and companion, Brutus. The fragrant smell of lavender from the blossoming lilacs filled the air for all creatures large and small to enjoy. Spring beckoned it's lure of renewal with sweetness. "Look, just as I thought; old man Rimstead waiting on the porch to check us out." Abe whispered. "I'm sure he'll be checking us out from top to bottom," quipped Zach whose face now lost its confidence and zealous smile. Greeted first by Brutus and his wagging tail the suitors then proceeded up the porch steps and were warmly welcomed with firm handshakes. "How you boys been doing? See that you washed behind your ears and slicked your hair," chuckled Philip. "Please sit yourself down as the girls are running a bit late. We just finished up doing the chores. I'll pour you a bit of refreshments while we wait." With the slam of the porch screen door Philip Rimstead left the two suitors grinning in silence for the unexpected warm welcome they were given. "Here we go, young fellows, a little drink to a warm spring evening," said Philip as he lifted his glass followed by... "bottoms up." He continued to chat with the two young McNabs. The slam of the porch screen door became a regular occurrence only to be followed by ..."another drink to" ... "and bottoms up". "That old geezer it trying to get us pissed. Each time he goes in to check if Sally and Sue are ready, he comes out with another drink," Abe groaned in disgust. "We'll soon be late for the show, Zach. "Old man Rimstead can't drink the two of us under the table if we take turns. I'll go first. Our only plan is to drink that old fart under the table if we are going to have any chance of seeing the girls," Abe smiled as he nodded approval.

"A drink to my beautiful daughters ...and bottoms up!

A drink to good heath ... and bottoms up!

A drink to a bountiful harvest...and bottoms up!"

As the 'bottoms up' continued, the spring evening was soon engulfed into darkness, as were the minds of two young would be suitors. With the approach of dawn, the McNab boys would find themselves in the family sedan in the same position they were when they first arrived. Their conceived plan had gone astray. Being young and naïve, they did not survive the doctoring of drinks at the hands of the wise old geezer. Embarrassed, Abe and Zach never returned to the farmstead of the beautiful blue-eyed blondes. As the years passed all the daughters left for the bright lights only to marry city slickers. Philip and Sadie Rimstead continued to farm and were blessed by many blonde, blue-eyed grandchildren that they dearly loved.

# Halloween Pranksters

Halloween tricks are now a fading rural occurrence. Prior to the onset of the prairie winters, trick or treating was a form of rural entertainment. The participants were not just the young, as many adults joined forces to partake in the high jinks to be bestowed upon their neighbours. Pranksters applied their trade with creativity only to be awarded with belly laughs and ... who done it! The harnessing of a pair of milk cows to a plough, the farm wagon, taken apart and reassembled on top of a hip roof barn, a litter of piglets, once white, dyed to the colour green, large rocks placed to block exits and the greasing of doorknobs were but a small sampling of some of the shenanigans that were carried out on Halloween night. But the most common was the toppling of the rural johnnie.

He was an eccentric farm bachelor and lived alone. His neighbours called him Pug. He sported a ponytail, a flattened nose and intense hazel eyes. Smitten with a love affair of books, visits to the local town library were his avenue of enjoyment. Pug was not a man of worldly treasures but a seeker of knowledge. Well versed in world affairs, his views were kept within. In the district, Pug held an air of mystique and his friends were few. Sam Stevenson, the owner of the local town paper would converse with Pug at times prior to editorials on world issues. His farm abode was a small one bedroom shack on the open prairie, surrounded by a hedge of hardy caragana. A short distance from the back door of the shack was the two-seater johnnie. It became an annual event in the farm district that Pug's outhouse would be toppled. Bragging rights and prowess were the norm for the Halloween tricksters as the task of upsetting Pug's johnnie became a challenge that grew in difficultly each year. Reinforced, bolted and tied down and a vigilant watch all ended with the same results.

One eventful Halloween day as dusk slowly crept in, Pug, with a shotgun in hand took up a guard position within. He settled down and patiently waited with the outhouse door slightly ajar. His plan was to capture or scare the tricksters as he knew that they would come before the morning dawn. The wait was not long. The tricksters had out foxed him. The johnnie door was quickly slammed shut and latched. As in previous years the front door hit the ground with a thud only this time with the owner inside. The obvious escape was practical but unpleasant. Pug being a wise man used the butt end of the shotgun and broke out the sidewall.

A year passed. A few days before Halloween, Pug made a trip into town. He stopped as usual at the library and visited the local paper owner, Sam Stevenson. A plan was laid. Moving his outhouse forward three to four feet he then carefully camouflaged the pit. The anchoring of the outhouse with ropes was a ploy and was portrayed as a challenge to the tricksters. As dusk approached, Pug took his post this time in his porch with shotgun in hand. A coal oil lamp lit the kitchen. Pug's silhouette was visible to those who may call. All seemed normal as it had been in years past. Hours ticked away. Pug waited patiently shifting his weight from foot to foot. He knew in his heart that they would come. But when? Were the anchor ropes too much of an obstacle for them brats, he thought to himself. Can't be. Had his plan been leaked? he wondered. Undeterred, Pug continued his vigilance. The night stillness was soon broken with screams of anguish and profanity. Like pouncing cats on a mouse, Pug and the hidden Sam Stevenson soon were on the scene. The blackness of the night was broken by bright flashes from Sam's camera. The three pranksters were caught in the pit and also on film. It was a Halloween prank that backfired. Bragging rights and self-esteem would vanish. In the local paper, the event on Pug's Halloween caper was shown for all the local folks to see. The caption under the picture read... "Halloween Gone Smelly."

Pug's johnnie stands the test of time. Pug was a wise man.

# Poetic Justice

It was early fall on a Sunday afternoon when my friend Don and I drove the country back roads scouting for an area to hunt the elusive whitetail deer. We were both avid bow and arrow hunters. To be successful, the prepared groundwork was a must. The scent of jack pine filled the autumn air as we motored along a small sandy road that was on the fringe of farmlands. To our surprise, tucked away amongst a cluster of aspen, pine and spruce was a small farmstead. A white clad cottage accompanied by a weathered red barn and corrals suddenly caught our eye. An elderly gentleman with a bucket in hand slowly made his way towards the barn as we drove into the lane. "Look in the corral!" Don blurted out in excitement. "Must be a dozen or so miniature horses." We were now in the horse business. Our deer project would be put on hold.

My friend Don, but only to himself, was the expert on the training, handling, doctoring and overall care of the horse.

"How ya-doing?" Don greeted the elderly gentleman with a beaming smile. "Nice looking ponies you have there." Don continued the chatter and had finally convinced the old farmer that he knew horses. "I can come over and trim their hoofs and de-worm them before winter, if you want," Don offered. "Well that would be just fine....by the way I'm Orest. Why don't you boys come on in for a spell. My wife went to visit her sister for the day," he commented. As Orest swung the now empty oat pail we followed him up a well-beaten path and settled down around the kitchen table. Large empty water glasses were soon placed before us. Grinning, Orest returned from the porch with an old rubber boot and placed it on the table. "We'll have a little doctoring for ourselves," he mused and reached into the boot and hanked out a bottle of vodka. "If my wife Stella finds any of my bottles, they are soon drained into the sink and besides, she gives me a tongue lashing unbecoming to any woman. If she caught us now I'm sure that she would have us all strung up in the barn," Orest chuckled. With a shaking hand the once empty glasses were filled to the brim. "Boys, the only way to drink vodka is straight up. No need for our kidneys to work overtime on extra liquid," Orest whispered softly, with a twinkle in his eye. We toasted each other to good health and sipped away the spirits. The tale that followed was an excuse for our glasses to be replenished.

"Last year just about this time I had a couple of yokels out in my hay field out back. I put my spyglasses on them and I could see that they were up to no good. I drove over in the pickup to kick them off my land. Them sons of guns were trespassing. The rotten bastards were target practicing with arrows into my hay bales." Taking a deep breath followed by healthy swallows of vodka, Orest continued, "I gave them hell. Those fellows were a bit obnoxious and cocky. They didn't think they were doing anything wrong. I told them that they better get their asses moving. I didn't need arrows in my horse feed. Their bows and cases were lying on the ground so I ran them over with the front wheel of my truck. That got their attention. I could hear them cussing as they picked up the pieces." Rising slowly from his chair, and removing the rubber boot from the table along with the empty vodka bottle, Orest made another trip back into the porch. "Look what I found in the other boot!" Holding a new source of vodka our glasses were again filled near their brim.

"A couple of weeks later I had a visit from the R.C.M.P. They said that I'd been charged with destroying property and must go to court. They informed me that I was being sued by those two bow hunters that I had run off. The R.C.M.P. were not interested in my side of the story and said that the matter would have to be settled in court. They had some sort of summons for me to go in front of the judge. Well, I and Stella had our day in front of the Justice. He wasn't the nicest to me after I explained the happenings. He told me I had no right to destroy other people's property and fined me the replacement costs of $300 or 30 days in jail. Case dismissed.

I went home a bit peeved and was burning up from the inside. I made up my mind to hold tight. Stella was all over me to be reasonable and pay the damm fine. You know me; I'm a stubborn cuss. I know what's right." Taking a short pause with a stern look in his eye, Orest continued. "They sent me a few notices demanding payment but they just made me dig in my heels. I pitched those notices in the burn barrel out back. I thought that would be the end of it.

It was mid winter and colder then hell when the R.C.M.P. came back and they read me my rights. You're off to jail for not obeying the Magistrates order. Like an old fool I said, ...take me away! One officer told me to pack my suitcase. I told him where to go. Take me as I am! They did just as they were told.

I left a note for Stella that I would be away for a month on a government job. I was escorted in the back of their car in a pair of dirty coveralls and rubber boots. I know those rubber boots were covered in horseshit. Those officers meant business and no fooling around." Seeing that our refreshments had evaporated, they were soon brought back to respectable levels by a now familiar shaking hand. "Darn if they didn't strip me down like a jay bird and fire me into a shower. A pretty little young nurse gives me a once over. She tells me to sit tight as a Doctor will come by for a further examination. To their surprise and mine, I'm a very sick man. "You can't go to jail in your condition, they advised me. "You're in need of a heart operation." Off to the hospital I went. They fitted me with a couple of pig valves. Stella tells me I now snore louder then any hog. I may one day end up rooting around in the garden."

Now laughing and blowing his nose, Orest pointed his finger at us. "The best part is that I spent a total of thirty five days in the hospital and rehabilitation house which was counted as time served. They then outfitted me with a new shirt, trousers, a jacket and dandy shoes! That's not all boys," Orest was now beaming from ear to ear. "I was driven home in a cab at the courts expense. I had the cabbie take me all around the country. It was a hella'va tour! That cab fare was over one hundred and fifty dollars. They did get something though .......I told them to keep my old clothes and boots! I knew I was right!" Those were the last words that summed up the tale of poetic justice.

We never did ask our storyteller for his permission to hunt on his lands but were offered the opportunity. My friend Don returned to trim hoofs and doctored the old man's horses.

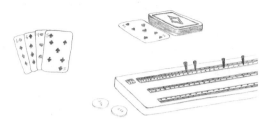

# Father Knows Best

A senior's home is where I met Adam. He was a soft-spoken and mild mannered man. Cribbage and tales of years passed were now his forte. I listened intently to his tales and realized that Adam was a man of integrity with the wisdom of a King Solomon. While we played crib his story unfolded.

"I homesteaded here in the district with my new wife, Hanna, in the dirty thirties. Times were hard but we made do like the rest of our neighbours. God was good to us and blessed us with twin sons. We named them Matthew and Mark. To complete the apostles, I told Hanna the next pair we'd call Luke and John, but we were never blessed with more children. God knew that two young boys would be a handful." Adam dealt the cards slowly as he tried to recall the past events more clearly. "As a family we attended regular Sunday church services. The rule on the farm forbid the use of alcohol and tobacco. It was Hanna's and my wish to see that our sons would grow into fine young men." With a winner's grin, Adam continued his story as we played crib with the two-bit wager.

"I remember it as if it was yesterday. It was a Saturday

morning and the farm yard was blanketed in a fresh covering of new snow. Unknown to me at the time, the boys had purchased a jug of red sherry wine. From the kitchen window Hanna and I noticed that our sons were making frequent trips to the barn. I became a bit suspicious so I posted a lookout in the hayloft and discovered their hidden treasure. The jug was carefully hidden under some hay at the front of the horse manger. My boys would take turns for a swig, first came Mark, and shortly after, in would come Matt. When the coast was clear, I removed a portion of the wine and carefully returned the jug to it's hiding place. I took some wine out after each son left. Before the end of the day the jug was just about empty. Well, it wasn't very long before a war of words developed! The boys began accusing each other for taking more than their fair share. Hanna and I watched in amusement from the kitchen window. Accusations intensified and the words turned into a wrestling match. The two boys reminded me of a couple of sparring young bulls. As I recall, Hanna and I played four games of cribbage as the boys continued to sort out their disagreement.

I then told the boys that Hanna and I were going into town for a few groceries. Since they were so full of energy, they could clean the barn out before Sunday. That got their attention. When we returned the barn was void of manure along with the jug." Getting back to the task at hand, Adam asked, "Whose crib?"

# An Angel or a Man

His name was Simon, a business associate of mine. A firm handshake, with no paper work, was all that would be needed in conducting our business. As the saying goes, he was as honest as the day is long. A lie he would not tell. Simon was a fine gentleman and family man. My acquaintance with Simon grew into a friendship that spanned more than twenty years.

The season was early fall. It was, as many times before, that I received a call from Simon to take a day trip into the foothills to do a bit of fishing and to hike a few trails. With packed lunches and fishing rods, we drove to the base of a trailhead and proceeded to hike to our favorite fishing hole. The fresh scent of pine filled our nostrils as we made our way up and down small valleys, only to be met by scampering squirrels that crossed our path. We were soon greeted by the sound of water as it came cascading down a small waterfall. A deep azure pool below rippled under a small breeze that gently buffed it's surface. Sunlight filtered through the quivering leaves of the aspen, setting the stage as we readied our fishing rods. This was surely heaven. As before, many brook trout soon graced our hooks only to be returned to the safety of the depths of the pool. Satisfaction and tranquility reigned. The sweetness of fresh mountain air rekindled our inner spirits and extinguished any worldly thoughts. We knew that we were very privileged to be experiencing mother nature at her very best. We pitied the poor souls that lived in the city's concrete jungle. I continued fishing as Simon made his way down stream. Shortly after I found my good friend fast asleep with his back nestled at the base of a gnarled old jackpine. His face was expressionless as his chest heaved with each breath. This was not the Simon I knew. Why would he want to sleep? At each pool down stream, trout were being taken on well-placed casts. No fly fisherman could have asked for any more.

When Simon awoke, he called me over. He tossed a large pebble in the center of the now placid pool. "Those ripples are your life. They start out strong and when they reach the shore they are gone. The strength of every following ripple lessens and soon there are no more. That's a fine example of life, my friend. A fine example." Taking a deep breath, Simon stared into the pool in deep thought. "I had a visit with the Doc the other day and results are not the best. I have to go in for cancer treatments in a couple of weeks. Maybe, I've just been around too long," he whispered as a wide smile crossed his face. "We'll be back here again. We'll be back my friend, we'll be back," were his words as we packed our gear and headed for home.

Three years had passed when I received a call from Simon. The season was early autumn. We had arranged to take our usual trip into the foothills to observe mother nature's masterful decoration of the painted landscape. Our fishing rods were left behind as Simon felt the hike to our favorite fishing hole might be too demanding.

It was a bright sunny day. Not a cloud appeared in the

brilliant blue sky. We had our lunches packed and drove to the trail head and found little had changed from years past. We built a small campfire and chatted and joked of our past business ventures and the scent of pine again refreshed our memories of past glories. As we were about to leave,

Simon came over to me and wrapped his arm around my shoulder. "I've something to tell you. When I was in the hospital for treatments a man came in to see me one day. He asked me what I wanted in life. I thought for a while and told him that I would like to see my grand children grow up before I die." He said, "Granted. I'll give you three years to live," and he then left. I asked the nurses and doctors who the man was that had come into my room to see me. They all said I had no visitor but I can still see his face as he stood at my bedside. Had I been dreaming? I have had three good years with my grandchildren and enjoyed every precious day with them," Simon remarked as he wiped a small tear from his cheek. "Those three years are now up and before the man left my room I told him we had a deal." I assured Simon to keep up the battle and that one day we would again take that hike up to our favorite fishing hole. "Hang in, I told him, just hang in. One day.... that day will come, Simon. One day..... that day will come." Just one week later I received a message that Simon had passed on. His service was held in a small country church which overflowed with friends and relatives who came to pay their last respects. Simon was laid to rest with the words that he was a honourable man with a great love for his family and friends.

After Simon's funeral service, I took a drive into the foothills and hiked up the trail to the fishing hole. The small waterfall now seemed quiet and sullen. The large deep pool displayed it's colours of greens and blues and lay placid. I tossed a large pebble into the pool as Simon had done before and watched the ripples run into shore. As the last faint ripple made its way to the outer edge, a large trout leapt from its depths. Was it a sign that Simon had returned to this place that he loved? I was filled with tranquility. Simon did not lie. His deal with the man, whoever he was, had been fulfilled. Simon was an honest man.

# An Unforgettable Dive

He sat in an old rocking chair on the front veranda. His warm brown eyes gazed out over vast fields of golden wheat that swayed gently under a warm fall breeze. He nodded and gave me a welcome wave as I made my way up the dirt path to the front steps. His name was Bartholomew Steel. Everyone, including his wife Rosie, called him BB.

"Sit yourself down," he commanded as he ran his fingers through a healthy stand of curly grey hair. "Would you care for a cup of tea or something a bit stronger? I'm ready for a little rum run," he quipped sheepishly. I nodded my approval for the same. As he rose from the rocking chair, he reminded me of a solid old oak tree; he stood tall and erect. He looked like a Greek god or athlete. His chiseled facial features and wavy hair still caught the eye of some local lady folk. He was held in high regard by neighbours. In his younger days, BB Steel's popularity among the county's young lassies soon drew the envy of other young courting gents. It was a given that every young lass wanted the arm of the young BB Steel. It was BB's easy pickings of pretty young ladies that orchestrated a plan among the other young gents for BB's downfall.

Kicking the screen door open, he soon returned with a bottle of rum under his arm with a tray of large water glasses, mix and pitcher of ice. "It's good that you dropped by as there's never a better time to top up one's anti freeze before winter sets in," he laughed. We chatted and toasted for health and a good harvest. A flock of cawing crows gathered in a bluff of popular as dusk approached. It was time for me to ask BB about his famous 'dive'. The rum bottle was now empty, making the question somewhat easier for me to ask and also for BB to answer. "I heard many versions of a dive you took in your early courting days at some country dance," I said sheepishly. "What's really the truth?" I asked, as I looked BB in the eye. "Well, it was no big deal. It was a way back many years ago on my twenty first birthday. Heck ...that's over forty years ago." Grinning mischievously, and rubbing his hands gently together, BB leaned back in his rocker and continued what I anxiously wanted to hear. "Well, I'm single and a-courtin' ....my birthday and a country dance are on the same day. What more could a fellow ask for? There would be all those pretty young ladies to dance with. I just loved to dance with those pretty country misses. I believed I even cleaned and washed down my old half-ton pick-up that day. True to my word I was dancing up a storm. Some of the local boys my age had lined up at the back of the hall and formed a stag line. I remember there were Billy and Tom Schmidt, and the McCallum boys and a few others. They never seemed to hit the dance floor but only watched the girls dance by. The band announced it was time to pick up your partner for the mid-night lunch. I made my way over to the beautiful Rosie who now is my good wife. As we danced the slow waltz, Rosie whispered something in my ear." Pausing and looking down at the floor, BB stopped to regain his thoughts. "Well, what did she whisper?" I asked with an impatient sigh. With a stern face BB stood up and raised his arms over his head and blurted out.... you're going to be black balled because it's your twenty first birthday you know!!!! The gang of boys at the back of the hall have a can of black shoe polish. They are just waiting for you to leave the hall." Now sitting down and rubbing his chin, a renewed sense of anger filled BB's voice. "Them dirty son's of bitches. I know there is too many of them to fight. I told Rosie I would make a run for it after lunch." His thoughts wandered as he watched the growing flock of cawing crows that were still gathering in the popular bluff. BB blew out a puff of air and remarked that the darn crows knew winter was coming. "So what happened next?" I asked, to get the story in progress again. "Well, I made a dash for the back door. That gang was right on my heels! I was running in full gear between a row of parked cars and heading for my truck. It then happened." "What happened?" I had to ask as I knew BB now had my full attention. "The dive! The dive! Just in front of me, up pops Mrs. Combs and old gramma Farley blocking the alley with their knickers down around their ankles. The johnnie out back must have been occupied. There was no room to get by so I dove for the only open spot. I hit the dirt only to find a pair of one of the ladies knickers wrapped around my neck. After that, I never missed a stride. I heard the gang hooting and hollering. I ran the six miles home and I picked up my truck the next morning. Some folks say that gramma Farley did a 360 in the air before she hit the ground. I can't vouch for the 360 but I know I missed being black balled." BB was now laughing and asked if I could keep a secret. "Sure, where are the lies in this story?" I asked. "No lies. As you know, not only did I marry the most gorgeous gal in the county, my Rosie; but I had the pleasure of mailing gramma Farley's knickers back to one of the blackballers C.O.D."

# April Fool Pranks

Many great episodes abound across the prairie landscape that would fill a book on April 1$^{st}$ foolery. Warped minds plotted ridiculous situations of "April Fool" to trick their neighbours or loved ones. Surprisingly, the more successful schemes of being had or hood winked, granted all parties the enjoyment of a good chuckle with no damage done.

It was on an early April 1$^{st}$ morning. The ritual for a group of farmers was their meeting at the local town coffee shop for a morning cup of freshly brewed java. Optimism ran high with the abatement of a long winter and an end to the calving season. The environment was ideal for devilish minds to conceive the most outlandish April 1$^{st}$ prank. Many ideas were bantered about in the group as the refills of coffee continued. More pranks than angles in a truckload of scrap iron were put forth. One idea stood out and was finally accepted. A telephone list was drawn up and Bernard, who had the most official sounding voice made the calls. Their wives would become the unsuspecting victims.

"This is your local telephone company. We are calling to inform you that after many years of service we are going to blow out the telephone lines. We suggest that you place your telephones in plastic bags to contain the dust and prevent it from filling your home. We will advise you once we have completed this operation. Thank you for your co-operation."

The pranksters, upon returning home for their noon meal found the phones encased in plastic bags and a lengthy explanation from their wives as to the reason.

# Moving

I was just a young lad of seven or so. My parents had just sold our farm and we were now moving to our new farm 300 or so miles farther north. This was an adventure for my younger sister and I. All our worldly possessions were loaded on a 3-ton truck that included my brand-new bicycle. The trip included a stop over at my Uncle's dairy farm where we spent the night. My Uncle advised my Dad to park the truck in a large shed to protect our meager belongings in the event of an over night rain. Early next morning my Uncle was out in the barnyard attending to chores. I was at the kitchen table with my Dad as he read the local paper and sipped on a coffee. I was absorbed in reading the comic sections. The silence was soon broken. The coffee, paper and comics went sailing through the air as we heard my Uncle holler, " Fire!......Fire!.......Fire in the shed!" I had never seen my Dad move with such speed. He ran down the gravel lane in his socks towards the shed and I followed behind in his giant footsteps. Losing my brand new bike was more than I could bear! My Uncle was standing in the barn doorway when we heard those famous words....... "April Fool !" My Dad's foreign vocabulary filled the air as I followed him back to the farm house.

After these many years I can still picture my father grumbling away as he sat barefoot at the kitchen table picking gravel and small rocks from his woolen socks.

# Metrics

It was the Federal Liberals under the fiuddle duddle Prime Minister Pierre Elliott Trudeau, that turned the farm folk into a state of confusion. Acre to hectare... pounds to kilo's.... inches to centimetres....yards to metres and the most feared was bushels to tonnes. Jake and Sally Martin were farm empty nest dwellers, and the debate of the metric system imposed upon them became daily conversation. On many occasions, opinions differed which led to Jake's "April Fools" prank.

Jake was a wisp of a man, pale, short, and with a dry sense of humor. His neighbour commented that he was like a dandelion plant trying to grow under a board. Sally, being the opposite, was tall, round and plump with a jovial disposition. "I'm running into town this morning for a few nails and wire", commented Jake as he buttered his toast. "Do you want to tag along?" asked Jake. "Not really, as I want to do a bit of laundry and curl my hair" replied Sally, as she carried her two poached eggs to the kitchen table. "Well, I heard the local Co-op hardware department has a sale on them new metric clocks. Guess we should pick one up before they run out," said Jake, as he scraped up a few breadcrumbs off his plate. "Metric time! What's this world coming to?   It's becoming a strange world we are now living in," commented Sally as she proceeded to eat her breakfast. "Yeah … there will be ten metric hours in a day and each hour will have one hundred metric minutes. That's a thousand metric minutes in a day. No more A.M.'s or P.M.s" Jake said sheepishly, as he scratched the end of his nose. "Heaven help us! I'd give that Trudeau the end of my mop if I ever got the chance. How long will a metric minute be?" asked Sally, now fully disgusted. "Just a thousand metric minutes in a ten hour metric day by my standards," quipped Jake. Sally said, "if we have to go metric time, I guess you better buy one. Make sure they are on sale though." With Sally's approval, Jake headed off to town.

Sally had a broom and dust pan in her hand as Jake entered the back porch upon his return. "Let me see that metric clock, Jake.  Did they still have any left?" asked Sally as Jake hung his coat on a wooden peg. "I've been fretting all morning about that ten hour metric day. Just can't believe it." Sally now waited in anticipation. "Well, they never sold out because there is no such thing, my dear wife. "April Fool!!" With that, Jake was chased around  the small farmhouse avoiding Sally's swinging  broom.

# My Harry

She sat under the shade of a large Manitoba maple tree. The air was filled with sweet essence from blossoming red clover. Bumble bees lumbered slowly from flower to flower at a lazy pace. Her name was Meg. She wore a wide brim straw hat with red straps that ended in a neat bow beneath her chin. In her lap was a heap of fresh picked peas that were being shelled. "My, it's getting hot and muggy this afternoon. Smells like rain. I can feel it in my bones," she said softly. "I knew you were coming to visit but not this early, I wanted to shell the peas before you came." She sighed and dumped the pea pods from her lap into a metal bucket that was at her side. "I have all day and I just wanted to see if you were still planning on living by yourself on the farm," I said. Meg rose and placed her hands on her hips, arched and stretched her back. "Damn right, I'll stay on this farm till the day I die. Harry or no Harry, I'll never move to town. I'm like an old dog. Enough said. If you want, you can finish shelling the peas." With that, Meg headed into the small farmhouse and returned with two large glasses of cold lemonade.

Harry was Meg's husband for forty-seven years; he died

the previous summer. They had two married daughters living in the city. Harry was a colourful character for those fortunate enough to have known him. The afternoon passed quickly as Meg reminisced about the happy times with her beloved Harry.

"I was a war bride. Harry, in his sweet way convinced me to marry him and move to Canada to the western prairies. If I knew then what the prairies were, I would have never come. I have grown to cherish this place. He told me he had cows and a ranch complete with a house. I can clearly recall him saying, "Honest... no bull!" After I arrived from England we were married down east. Shortly after, we moved out west and I set foot on this homestead in early spring. Yes, indeed he did have cows - a total of four and no bull!" Smiling, Meg took a hand full of peas pods and placed them in her lap. "The house back then was an old granary. My God, I said to myself what have I gotten into? After our first night in our new home I found that in the morning my body was covered in round welts. I was dumb founded. I soon discovered the welts came from the knotholes in the slab boards under a very thin straw mattress." Rubbing her arms and waist as if the welts were still there, Meg sighed and continued to tell me about her earlier days on the homestead. "We worked very hard and made do with what we had. Those were care free days and the best of times." Meg sheepishly grinned and blurted out, "Harry and I made 'MOOSE MILK'! It was quite an adventure. We used what we had at hand, wheat, berries, raisins, potatoes, dandelions and even rhubarb. The leftover mash we fed to our few pigs. It put them in pig paradise as they slept and snored for most of the day. Oh my, how quickly time has passed." Meg was now in high spirits. "My Harry always wore a smile. That's what I loved about him. One night he awoke with a fever and chills and was in a bit of a stupor. On came his brand new pair of woolen long johns that I had just purchased. Oh my poor Harry. Nature urgently called!" Meg was now holding her sides in uncontrollable laughter. "He soon realized there was no trap door. In a panic he ran to the kitchen and grabbed a butcher knife and made a new doorway. Oh my! In the morning he awoke with a smile. On inspection he had found two trap doors; the original, with a button high on his back and the newly created opening." Wiping the tears from her cheeks, Meg went on to explain that Harry had done a reverse. "In his frenzy he had put his legs in the sleeves and arms in as legs. With many memories like this, how can I possibly leave this place?" she asked me.

Meg now finished her lemonade and looked into the western sky that was filling with puffy white clouds. "Not in a minute would I leave this place. It has too many good memories for me. It's been my life's work. This is my place. This is where I plan to die as has my Harry. This place is me."

For additional copies of Stories, Lies That Farmers Have Told Me, please contact your local book store or publisher. To arrange author interviews, special events or book signings contact:

Grey Wolf Publishing
6429-111A Street
Edmonton Ab.  T6H  3H7

Phone: [ 780 ]  436- 4017
email:  james007@telusplanet.net